FIELD GUIDE

to

BUTTERFLIES

of

THE GAMBIA, WEST AFRICA

by Dr David Penney

The butterfly counts not months but moments, and has time enough.

Rabindranath Tagore

ISBN 978-0-9558636-2-2

Published by Siri Scientific Press, Manchester, UK
This and similar titles are available directly from the publisher at:

http://www.siriscientificpress.co.uk

This book was designed, written, type set and published entirely within the UK by the author and Siri Scientific Press.

Contents

Photographic Section

INTRODUCTION & SCOPE

The Gambia is located on the Atlantic coast of tropical West Africa between latitudes 13 and 14 degrees north, with an open coastline of 70 km and is otherwise surrounded by Senegal for its entire land border of 740 km. There is a sheltered coastline of 200 km along the River Gambia dominated by extensive mangrove systems and mudflats. The Gambia loosely tracks the course of the river as it meanders inland (the river originates in Guinea and flows from east to west) and with an area of only 11,295 km^2 (10,000 km^2 of dry land) is the smallest country on the continent. In contrast to many other West African countries it is relatively flat, with the highest point less than 100 m above sea level. The country is situated on the Continental Terminal, a vast Tertiary sandstone plateau, which originated from the iron-rich soils to the east. These were eroded from the continent into the Atlantic and then over millions of years redeposited against the coastline and lithified (turned to stone).

The sub-tropical climate is pleasant, with two distinct seasons determined by the imbalance at the boundary of the high-pressure regions north and south of the equator (the ITCZ: inter-tropical convergence zone). Generally speaking, November to June consist of dry savannah winds (Harmattan), whereas from July to October the country sees heavy downpours and is lusciously green. Even in the height of the rainy season it does not rain every day and much of the rainfall occurs overnight. There are still many days of uninterrupted sunshine, but the high humidity can be rather oppressive towards the end of the rainy season. However, Gambian biodiversity is at its most spectacular during the rains, not least because they initiate an explosion of a great diversity of flowering plants and a visit at this time of year is highly recommended.

The population of the country is nearly 1.7 million, increasing annually with a growth rate of approximately 2.7%. Given that the major economic activities within The Gambia, such as agriculture, agro-processing, fisheries, livestock production and tourism have quite specific land usage requirements, the increasing population size and the subsequent increase in demand for these products will undoubtedly affect the relative abundance and distribution of the various habitat types present in the country. What the knock-on effects of this will be for Gambian wildlife is unclear. However, in an interesting paper, Larsen (2008) suggested that forest butterflies were relatively resistant to extinction and that no species had become regionally extinct in West Africa, despite heavy deforestation over the last century and a half. Larsen believes the findings are an argument for improved conservation of the remaining forests in West Africa.

The Gambia lies within the transition zone at the interface of relatively moist Guinean forest–savannah mosaic in the south and the drier Sudanian woodlands in the north. Within this system, the country supports many diverse habitat types including marine and coastal, estuary and mangrove, banto faros (barren hypersaline flats derived from the mangroves), brackish and freshwater river banks, swamp forest, freshwater swamps and other wetlands (e.g., bolons, rice fields, ponds, etc.; obviously more prominent during the rainy season), forest (primary coastal e.g., Bijilo, primary gallery e.g., Abuko, secondary e.g., Tanji, etc.) and woodland, forest–savannah mosaic, villages, farmland and fallow land.

Such a diverse range of habitat types can be expected to contain a high biodiversity of indigenous plants and animals, in addition to naturalized introductions and migrant species. This is certainly the case, but our knowledge of the fauna and flora is far from complete and differs significantly for different groups. In general, those groups that are useful (e.g., for building materials, have medicinal properties, are edible, are dangerous to humans or their crops) tend to be better known than less so-called useful groups. Although butterflies do not fit easily into any of these groups, they are perhaps the best known insect order in The Gambia, as is true for many other tropical regions of the world. This is because they are active during the day and highly apparent, resulting from their relatively large size and bright colours (when compared to many other insect groups). They are abundant in terms of numbers of individuals and it is hard not to see a butterfly on even a short walk...or just sitting around for that matter. At present, none of the butterflies recorded from The Gambia are considered endemic (i.e., all the species also occur elsewhere in West Africa).

BIOLOGY & ECOLOGY

Butterflies and moths belong to the order Lepidoptera. Although there is no firm distinction between them, the general rules are that butterflies tend to have bright colours, clubbed antennae, rest with their wings held together (except some skippers) and have a pupal stage without a cocoon. In addition, they tend to be diurnal (active during the day), whereas most moths are nocturnal. However, there are exceptions. Many skippers (Hesperiidae) and browns (Satyrinae) are crepuscular (fly at dawn and dusk) and some of the tiger moth subfamilies are brightly coloured and fly during the day. Adult butterflies are characterized by possessing two pairs of large, membranous wings covered with fine scales, and sucking mouthparts produced into an elongated proboscis that forms a tight coil when not in use.

It is the wing scales that produce the beautiful colours of some butterfly species. The tiny scales, which develop from the wing epidermal cells, number in the thousands and overlap one another. It is these that rub off on the hand when a butterfly is handled. There is great variation in shape and colour, with much of the colour produced by pigment molecules within the scale. However, the metallic iridescence seen in some species is as a result of a combination of structural colours and the interference of light as it bounces off the scale. The recent discovery that in butterflies the scales also function as solar collectors has led scientists to produce butterfly wing templates in the manufacture of new light-harvesting technologies, which have shown an increase in efficiency over conventional methods.

The life cycle of butterflies is a complete metamorphosis and consists of four stages. Adult females deposit eggs on or near an appropriate food plant. After approximately one week the larva (caterpillar) hatches out, first consuming the eggshell before starting on the food plant. Caterpillars are basically feeding machines and do so at an incredible rate, shedding their skin four times as they increase in size. After several weeks the larva develops into a hardened pupa in which the transformation to the imago (adult form) takes place. When fully developed, the pupa ruptures along defined sutures and the butterfly forces its way out. Over the next several hours the adult pumps body fluids into the veins of its wings and they gradually expand and harden. In some species of blue butterflies (family Lycaenidae), the larvae are reared inside the nests of ants by their hosts. The correct term for this is myrmecophily. In the Common woolly legs *Lachnocnema emperamus* the larva is carnivorous, feeding on homopteran bugs. The caterpillars of many butterfly species have quite specific food plant preferences, whereas others will eat a great variety of different flora and are known as polyphagous.

Some butterflies sequester noxious compounds (as caterpillars) from their food plants and use them in their own defence against predators. The African tiger *Danaus chrysippus chrysippus* is one such species, which has traditionally been considered as unpalatable to predators when the larvae have fed on plants containing cardiac glycosides. However, at least one recent study has questioned whether or not all individuals are truly distasteful. The butterflies are brightly coloured to warn predators of their bad taste. Such warning colours are known as aposematic coloration. Some non-poisonous species mimic the poisonous species, which is termed the model. In The Gambia (and elsewhere in Africa), the Diadem *Hypolimnas misippus* mimics the African tiger in order to benefit from protection against predators. This is known as Batesian mimicry, but in order for it to be successful the mimic needs to be less abundant than the model. Thus, there is a cost to the mimic in terms of limits to its population size. This is partly overcome in the Diadem by only having the female as the mimic. Indeed, the male is so strikingly different from the female that they could easily be confused for two different species by a general observer. This phenomenon is known as sexual dimorphism. Other forms of dimorphism include seasonal variation (see NOTES ON SEASONALITY after the checklist), geographical variation of isolated populations during the process of speciation and polymorphism, where numerous different forms of the same species exist.

Most butterflies feed on nectar from flowers, although some species do not feed at all in the adult stage. The weed of wasteland *Tridax procumbens* is a particular favourite for many species. Other flowers much loved by many species include the butterfly bush *Lantana camara*, the labiate *Hoslundia opposita* (both common in

Lantana camara

Hoslundia opposita

Stachytarpheta indica

Tridax procumbens

forest clearings) and the ornamental *Stachytarpheta indica* (common in and around local compounds). Several species of skipper often feed on animal droppings, for example the Striped policeman *Coeliades forestan forestan* and Clouded flat *Tagiades flesus* on bird droppings and the Common grizzled skipper *Spialia spio* on cow dung. Many nymphalids, such as Charaxes, obtain fluids from sucking holes on trees and from rotting fruit and may return to the same spot day after day. An unusual behaviour of many species is the extraction of salts through imbibing large quantities of fluid from the ground. This behaviour is known as mud-puddling. Sometimes vast numbers of individuals can be seen mud-puddling at the same place. Males of some species are highly territorial and select a high point from which to defend their territory against rival males. This behaviour is known

Tagiades flesus at bird dropping

Spialia spio on cow dung

Charaxes varanes at sucking hole

Belenois aurota mud-puddling

as hill-topping. In some species males select a good spot for perching or patrol a particular area in search of females.

Butterflies have many enemies in their natural habitat through all stages of their life cycle, and some scientists estimate that a single female will suffer in excess of 95% mortality of all progeny produced. Probably the most important in the early stages are parasitic wasps (Hymenoptera) and flies (Diptera), in addition to bacterial, viral and fungal infections. As adults they form prey for a whole range of invertebrates including mantids, robber flies, spiders and dragonflies, in addition to birds, lizards, frogs and some mammals. If you see a butterfly that does not fly away as you approach it, look very carefully and you will probably find a well camouflaged crab spider (Thomisidae) attached to it!

Mantis preying on Nymphalidae

Robber fly preying on Pieridae

Crab spider preying on Lycaenidae

Dragonfly preying on Pieridae

Many butterfly species have evolved means to avoid becoming a tasty meal for another animal. These include defensive chemicals, which make them taste unpleasant (at least to vertebrates), crypsis and mimicry, a nervous disposition with rapid erratic flight, and also a phenomenon termed self mimicry. In the last instance, butterflies have false eye spots on the hindwings and also thin tails that wiggle around and resemble antennae. In effect, these give the impression of the head being at the wrong end of the body, and this tends to be more attractive to predators than the actual head itself. If the real head were to be bitten off then the butterfly would surely perish. However, the loss of a portion of the hindwing gives the individual a second chance and it is not uncommon to see specimens in the field with these areas of the hindwings missing.

Thank you for purchasing one of our titles.
We hope you enjoy it. We would love it if you
purchased your next SSP book directly from us as this
helps greatly with our production of new volumes.
As a thank you we would like to offer you a

12.5% LOYALTY
DISCOUNT

when you purchase directly from our website
using this code at checkout: **AMZ2016**
(we ship worldwide)

*From our website you can also follow us on Facebook or
check out our blog, where we keep you up-to-date
with new title releases and special offers.
Take a look today.*

SSP
SIRI SCIENTIFIC PRESS

Thank you Daniel

Titles you may be interested in:

- Field Guide to Wildlife of The Gambia
- Common Spiders and other arachnids of The Gambia.

**Are you interested in joining our expanding authorship of leading
international experts from major academic
institutions worldwide? (see overleaf)**

http://www.siriscientificpress.co.uk
e-mail: books@siriscientificpress.co.uk

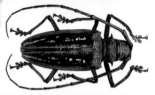

SIRI SCIENTIFIC PRESS

Why publish your book, monograph or edited volume with *Siri Scientific Press*?

Some quotes from our authors, customers & reviewers:

I'm really pleased with this volume and want to thank you for the incentive and for all the hard work of putting it together. It will be an excellent resource for many years to come and an inspiration to students to take up challenges in spider research (Prof., Ben-Gurion University [author])

You have done a brilliant job in the production of it – congratulations (Dr., Natural History Museum, London [customer])

Editing of "biodiversity of fossils in amber" was one of the best ideas in the last decade (Germany [customer])

It looks really nice, I just ordered a second copy for our departmental display case (Prof., University of Massachusetts [author])

Splendid! Very well done and with a perfect lay-out … You did a very efficient and no-nonsense job. Thanks a lot (Dr., Royal Museum for Central Africa [author])

Your layouts are beautiful! The book is clearly on its way to becoming something that we will be very proud of. I cannot thank you enough! (USA [author])

Just received the book, and it's a cracker! Thanks for making it a reality (Dr., Dorset [author])

An absolutely exemplary editor and publisher (Prof., University of Essex [author])

SSP has quickly made a name for itself in producing high-quality scientific books and monographs that deal with natural history. Admitted, SSP has a niche product, but one that they excel at producing (Prof., USA [academic reviewer, Priscum 2015])

...produced to a very high standard, with numerous colour images, all printed on good quality paper. The editing is tight and as far as I can tell, error-free (Newsletter of the British Arachnological Society [academic book review])

We ensure a speedy yet professional & personal service at all times.
To maintain the highest quality we do not use print-on-demand publishing.
We support local businesses committed to minimal environmental impact.
Our titles get excellent reviews & are taken by academic libraries worldwide.

For more information please visit our website:
http://www.siriscientificpress.co.uk *or* e-mail: books@siriscientificpress.co.uk
We are always happy to hear from potential new authors; thank you for your interest
We reserve the right to remove any discount offers from our website at any time

A WEST AFRICAN CONTEXT

The butterflies of West Africa are extremely diverse, as might be expected for a tropical region. However, the butterfly fauna of The Gambia is not particularly species rich, although a definitive list of unambiguous identifications does not currently exist. According to Larsen (2005) virtually no real forest species occur in The Gambia and many of the Sahel species are also absent. However, that is not to say that the Gambian butterfly fauna is not interesting. Because the country lies at the transition zone between moist Guinean Savannah in the south and the drier Sudanian Savannah in the north there is an interesting mix of species considered as typical for each major habitat type. For example, according to Larsen (2005) the Small monk *Amauris damocles* (Gambian record questionable), Angular bush brown *Bicyclus angulosus*, Rock bush brown *B. pavonis*, Lesser rock bush brown *B. milyas*, Condamin's three-ring *Ypthima condamini*, Vuattoux's ringlet *Y. vuattouxi*, Elegant acraea *Acraea egina*, Abject hopper *Astictopterus abjecta*, Morant skipper *Parosmodes morantii*, Small swift *Borbo perobscura* and Hottentot skipper *Gegenes hottentota* are typical of Guinean Savannah, whereas the Zebra white *Pinacopteryx eriphia*, Veined golden arab *Colotis vesta*, Scarlet tip *C. danae*, Purple tip *C. ione*, Large orange tip *C. antevippe*, Blue savannah sapphire *Iolaus menas*, Savannah pied pierrot *Tuxentius cretosus*, most pierrots of the genus *Tarucus*, Common three-ring *Ypthima asterope*, Cream-bordered charaxes *Charaxes epijasius*, Bush charaxes *C. achaemenes*, Savannah demon charaxes *C. viola*, Blue pansy *Junonia orithya*, Orange elfin *Sarangesa phidyle*, Olive-haired swift *Borbo borbonica* and Pigmy skipper *Gegenes 'pumilio' gambica* are indicative of Sudanian Savannah, yet all occur within The Gambia. In addition, several primarily Sahelian species are also components of the Gambian butterfly fauna, including the Milky bean cupid *Euchrysops nilotica*, Sky-blue cupid *Chilades eleusis* and Desert babul blue *Azanus ubaldus*, the last of which represents a new species record for the country.

Previous data on Gambian butterflies include a study of skippers by Gillies (1982), a checklist of 75 species by Newport (1993) and an unpublished, annotated checklist with some photographs by Newport (1998), which listed 109 species, including many new records from single specimens. Barnett, Emms & Newport (2003) produced a short pamphlet illustrating 60 common species, with no additional information on those not included, some of which are more common than some of those that were. Penney (2009) provided close up photographs of live specimens for 54 species. A provisional checklist of all biota recorded from The Gambia published online by the Makasutu Wildlife Trust (Emms & Barnett, 2005, updated 2006; this no longer appears to be available) listed 174 butterfly species as follows: Papilionidae (4 spp.), Pieridae (25 spp.), Lycaenidae (47 spp.), Nymphalidae (56 spp.) and Hesperiidae (42 spp.). However, it should be noted that the reliability of this data resource has proven to be questionable for some other groups. An unpublished manuscript on the butterflies of Senegambia (basically an annotated key in French) by Condamin (ca. 1986) listed approximately 250 species for the region, but contained very few Gambian specific records, with most originating from Basse Cassamance and Niokolo Koba in Senegal.

Larsen (2005) covered the butterflies of all West Africa, providing details and figures of more than 1,450 species. This is a fabulous and monumental work, which is a must for anybody with a serious interest in butterflies of The Gambia. However, it is expensive and occupies two large volumes, making it impractical to take out in the field. The following list (based primarily on data from Larsen (2005) consists of 170 species in five families as follows: Papilionidae (4 spp.), Pieridae (26 spp.), Lycaenidae (50 spp.), Nymphalidae (54 spp.) and Hesperiidae (36 spp.); none of them are endemic. Five of the species represent new records for the country (see end of checklist for further details) and some of these species are encountered reasonably frequently. Thus, additional new records should not be unexpected, even in the better-studied Western Division as well as further inland.

CHECKLIST OF GAMBIAN BUTTERFLIES

As with most groups of invertebrate animals, there is much debate about that classification of butterflies, particularly with regard to supra-ordinal (tribe, subfamily etc.) designations. New techniques, such as advanced computer cladistic analysis for constructing evolutionary trees and DNA analysis will help resolve these issues in the future.

*indicates that the species is illustrated in this field guide
~indicates a new species record for The Gambia
?indicates a questionable record/status in The Gambia unclear
†indicates the species is possibly extinct in The Gambia
numbers in parentheses following each species refer to the numbers in Larsen (2005) to facilitate cross referencing for further information; G = recorded in Gillies (1982), N = recorded in Newport (1993); NW = recorded in Newport (1998), B = recorded in Barnett *et al.* (2003); taxonomy follows Larsen (2005)

Superfamily PAPILIONOIDEA
Family PAPILIONIDAE

The swallowtail butterflies are so called because of the tail-like extensions on the edge of the hindwing, which are present in many, but not all species. They do not occur in any of The Gambian species. This family represents the least diverse butterfly family in The Gambia, but all species are reasonably common. All are large and colourful, with both sexes similar in appearance and all Gambian species are easily recognizable on the wing, even by the novice.

Subfamily PAPILIONINAE
PAPILIO
Narrow-banded green swallowtail P. nireus nireus (11)[N,NW,B]
Citrus swallowtail P. demodocus demodocus (13)[N,NW,B]

GRAPHIUM
White lady G. angolanus baronis (20)[N,NW,B]
Veined swallowtail G. leonidas leonidas (29)[N,NW,B]

Family PIERIDAE

The yellow-white butterflies are usually pale coloured and of small to medium size. They are some of the most common butterflies, especially during mass migrations of certain species (see NOTES ON SEASONALITY following the checklist). Some of the species are remarkably similar and difficult to separate on the wing. This is true of the orange tips, the yellows and some of the whites, although with some experience many of the species tend to have their own 'jizz', to use an ornithological term.

Subfamily COLIADINAE
CATOPSILIA
***African emigrant** C. florella* (36)[N,NW,B]

EUREMA
***Common grass yellow** E. hecabe solifera* (39)[N,NW,B]
***Small grass yellow** E. brigitta brigitta* (43)[N,NW,B]

Subfamily PIERINAE
Tribe Pierini
PINACOPTERYX
***Zebra white** P. eriphia tritogenia* (44)[N,NW,B]

NEPHERONIA
***Large vagrant** N. argia argia* (45)
***?Blue vagrant** N. thalassina thalassina* (46)

COLOTIS
Small salmon arab *C. amata amata* (51)[N,NW]
Veined golden arab *C. vesta amelia* (54)
Magenta tip *C. celimene sudanicus* (57)[Newport pers. communication]
***Purple tip** C. ione* (58)
***Scarlet tip** C. danae eupompe* (60)[N,NW,B]
Sulphur orange tip *C. aurora evarne* (61)
***Large orange tip** C. antevippe antevippe* (62)[N,NW]
Round-winged orange tip *C. euippe euippe* (63)[N,NW]
***Tiny orange tip** C. evagore antigone* (65)[N,NW,B]
Banded gold tip *C. eris eris* (67)

BELENOIS
***Caper white** B. aurota* (68)[N,NW,B]

African caper white B. creona creona* (69)[N,NW]
***Pointed caper white** B. gidica gidica* (70)[N,NW]
***Calypso caper white** B. calypso calypso* (73)[N,NW,B]

DIXEIA
***Creamy small white** D. orbona orbona* (79)[N,NW,B]

PONTIA
Desert white *P. glauconome* (83)

APPIAS
Common albatross *A. sylvia sylvia* (84)[NW]
***African albatross** A. epaphia epaphia* (87)[N,NW]

LEPTOSIA
***African spirit** L. alcesta alcesta* (88)[N,NW,B]

MYLOTHRIS
***Common dotted border** M. chloris chloris* (95)[N,NW,B]

Family LYCAENIDAE

The blues, coppers, hairstreaks, etc. form a diverse family of very small to medium-sized butterflies. There is great variation in terms of morphology, colour and natural history. Many species have a fast and erratic flight and can be difficult to identify on the wing. Even at rest, identification of some species is impossible from a distance because many are confusingly similar in appearance. Indeed, some are so similar that dissection and microscopic examination of the genitalia are required in order to confirm the correct species identification. In terms of recorded species, this family represents the second most diverse butterfly family in The Gambia after the Nymphalidae. However, given that four of the five new species records listed here are lycaenids, the expectation is that more still remain to be documented for the country. This family is probably the most diverse in The Gambia and it is certainly the most abundant in terms of numbers of individuals.

Subfamily MILETINAE
Tribe Spalgini

15

SPALGIS
African apefly *S. lemolea pilos* (130)

Tribe Lachnocnemini
LACHNOCNEMA
***Common woolly legs** *L. emperamus* (133)

Subfamily Lipteninae
Tribe Epitolini
?CEPHETOLA
?Roche's epitola *C. subcoerulea* (300)

Subfamily Theclinae
Tribe Amblypodiini
MYRINA
***Common fig blue** *M. silenus silenus* (354)[N,NW,B]
~***Small fig blue** *M. subornata subornata* (355)

Tribe Loxurini
DAPIDODIGMA
Western virgin *D. hymen* (359)[NW]

Tribe Aphnaeini
APHNAEUS
***Common silver spot** *A. orcas* (361)[NW]

APHARITIS
Saharan silverline *A. nilus* (368)

SPINDASIS
***Common silverline** *S. mozambica* (369)[NW]

AXIOCERSES
***Common scarlet** *A. harpax* (375)[N,NW,B]

Tribe IOLAINI
IOLAUS
Subgenus *Iolaphilus*
***Blue savannah sapphire** *I. menas menas* (393)[N,NW]
Subgenus *Philiolaus*

16

Druce's sapphire *I. lukabas* (403)
Large green sapphire *I. calisto* (407)
Subgenus *Epamera*
~*__Scintillating sapphire__ *I. scintillans* (414)
*__Iasis sapphire__ *I. iasis iasis* (436)[N,NW]

Tribe Hypolycaenini
HYPOLYCAENA
*__Common hairstreak__ *H. philippus philippus* (443)[N,NW,B]

Tribe Deudorigini
PILODEUDORIX
Green-streaked playboy *P. diyllus occidentalis* (458)
Blue heart playboy *P. caerulea caerulea* (460)

DEUDORIX
*__Common brown playboy__ *D. antalus* (494)[N,NW,B]
Pomegranate playboy *D. livia* (495)[N,NW]
Coffee playboy *D. lorisona abriana* (496)
Apricot playboy *D. dinochares* (498)[NW]

Subfamily POLYOMMATINAE
Tribe Lycaenesthini
ANTHENE
~*__Light ciliate blue__ *A. liodes liodes* (512)
*__Leaden ciliate blue__ *A. amarah* (516)[N,NW,B]
Red-spot ciliate blue *A. lunulata* (517)[NW]
*__Common ciliate blue__ *A. larydas* (523)[N,NW,B]
Crawshay's ciliate blue *A. crawshayi crawshayi* (524)[NW]

TRICLEMA
Nigerian ciliate blue *T. nigeriae* (556)

Tribe Polyommatini
PSEUDONACADUBA
African line blue *P. sichela sichela* (565)[N,NW]

LAMPIDES
*__Pea blue__ *L. boeticus* (567)[N,NW,B]

CACYREUS
Common bush blue *C. lingeus* (575)[N,B]

LEPTOTES[N]
Common zebra blue *L. pirithous* (578)[NW]
Babault's zebra blue *L. babaulti* (579)[NW]

TUXENTIUS
Savannah pied pierrot *T. cretosus nodieri* (583)[N,NW,B]

TARUCUS
Ungemach's pierrot *T. ungemachi* (586)[NW]
African pierrot *T. theophrastus* (587)[N,NW]
Mediterranean pierrot *T. rosacea* (588)[N,NW]

EICOCHRYSOPS
White-tipped cupid *E. hippocrates* (593)

EUCHRYSOPS
Smoky bean cupid *E. malathana* (601)[N,NW]
Milky bean cupid *E. nilotica* (602)
African cupid *E. osiris* (604)[N,NW]

LEPIDOCHRYSOPS
Untailed blue giant cupid *L. synchrematiza* (611)[N,NW,B]

AZANUS
~**Desert babul blue** *A. ubaldus* (627)
African babul blue *A. jesous* (628)[NW]
Black-bordered babul blue *A. moriqua* (629)[N,NW]

CHILADES
Sky-blue cupid *C. eleusis* (633)[N,NW,B]
Grass jewel *C. trochylus* (634)

ZIZEERIA
African grass blue *Z. knysna* (635)[N,NW,B]

ZIZINA
Dark grass blue *Z. antanossa* (636)[N,NW]

ZIZULA
Tiny grass blue *Z. hylax* (637)

Family NYMPHALIDAE
The brush-footed butterflies include the monarchs, browns, fritillaries, pansies, charaxes and acraeas. It is the most species rich family in the world and also for The Gambia in terms of recorded species (although see the note under Lycaenidae). Nymphalids are medium to very large-sized butterflies and are some of the most beautiful butterflies in The Gambia. Most species are readily identifiable on the wing, although the browns and a few of the acraeas can be problematic.

Subfamily Danainae
Tribe Danaini
DANAUS
Subgenus *Anosia*
*****Common tiger** *D. chrysippus chrysippus* (647)[N,NW,B]

AMAURIS
Subgenus *Amaura*
?**Small monk** *A. damocles damocles* (653)

Subfamily Satyrinae
Tribe Melanitini
MELANITIS
*****Common evening brown** *M. leda* (658)[NW,B]
*****Violet-eyed evening brown** *M. libya* (659)

Tribe Elymniini
BICYCLUS
Western large bush brown *B. zinebi* (673)
Rock bush brown *B. pavonis* (679)
Lesser rock bush brown *B. milyas* (680)[NW]
*****Vulgar bush brown** *B. vulgaris* (690)[N,NW,B]
Dark vulgar bush brown *B. sandace* (692)
Angular bush brown *B. angulosus angulosus* (698)[NW,B]
Common savannah bush brown *B. safitza safitza* (701)
Funereal bush brown *B. funebris* (702)

Tribe Satyrini
YPTHIMA
*Common three-ring *Y. asterope asterope* (715)
Condamin's three-ring *Y. condamini nigeriae* (716)
Vuattoux's ringlet *Y. vuattouxi* (718)

YPTHIMOMORPHA
Swamp ringlet *Y. itonia* (724)[NW,B]

Subfamily CHARAXINAE
Tribe Charaxini
CHARAXES
*Pearl charaxes *C. varanes vologeses* (725)[N,NW,B]
*?Green-veined charaxes *C. candiope candiope* (728)
?Flame-bordered charaxes *C. protoclea protoclea* (729)
*Bamboo charaxes *C. boueti* (730)
*Cream-bordered charaxes *C. epijasius* (734)[N,NW,B]
*Giant charaxes *C. castor castor* (736)
*Bush charaxes *C. achaemenes atlantica* (755)[N,NW,B]
*Savannah demon charaxes *C. viola viola* (770)[N,NW,B]

Subfamily NYMPHALINAE
Tribe Nymphalini
VANESSA
*Painted lady *V. cardui* (791)[N,NW,B]

Tribe Junoniini
PRECIS
*Darker commodore *P. antilope* (793)[N,NW,B]

HYPOLIMNAS
*Diadem *H. misippus* (801)[N,NW,B]
*Variable eggfly *H. anthedon anthedon* (802)

JUNONIA
*Blue pansy *J. orithya madagascariensis* (813)[NW]
*Dark blue pansy *J. oenone oenone* (814)[N,NW,B]
*Yellow pansy *J. hierta cebrene* (815)[N,NW,B]
*Little commodore *J. sophia sophia* (819)[N,NW,B]
*Golden pansy *J. chorimene* (822)[N,NW,B]

*Soldier pansy *J. terea terea* (823)[N,NW]

CATACROPTERA
*Pirate *C. cloanthe ligata* (824)

Subfamily BIBLIDINAE
Tribe Eurytelini
BYBLIA
*African joker *B. anvatara crameri* (826)[N,NW,B]

Subfamily LIMENITIDINAE
Tribe Limenitidini
NEPTIS
*River sailer *N. serena serena* (905)[N,NW,B]

Tribe Adoliadini
HAMANUMIDA
*Guineafowl *H. daedalus* (951)[NW,B]

BEBEARIA
*†Senegal palm forester *B. senegalensis* (1013)[N,NW,B]

EUPHAEDRA
Subgenus *Medoniana*
*Widespread forester *E. medon pholus* (1046)[NW]
Subgenus *Euphaedrana*
*Ceres forester *E. ceres ceres* (1083)

Subfamily HELICONIINAE
Tribe Acraeini
ACRAEA
Subgenus *Actinote*
*Encedon acraea *A. encedon encedon* (1153)
?Encedana acraea *A. encedana* (1154)
*Small orange acraea *A. serena* (1159)[N,NW,B]
*Bonasia acraea *A. bonasia bonasia* (1165)[NW]
Subgenus *Acraea*
*Elegant acraea *A. egina egina* (1176)[NW,B]
*Abadima acraea *A. pseudegina* (1178)[N,NW]

21

*Pink acraea *A. caecilia caecilia* (1179)[N,NW,B]
*Large spotted acraea *A. zetes zetes* (1180)[N,NW,B]
*Common glassy acraea *A. quirina quirina* (1184)
Wandering donkey *A. neobule neobule* (1185)[NW]
Large smoky acraea *A. camaena* (1187)
Clouded bematistes *A. umbra carpenteri* (1190)

Tribe Vagrantini
PHALANTA
*Common leopard fritillary *P. phalantha aethiopica* (1200)[N,NW,B]

Superfamily HESPERIOIDEA
Family HESPERIIDAE

The skippers are currently placed in an unresolved trichotomy, with the aforementioned true butterfly families and the Hedylidae (American butterfly moths) in a group called Rhopalocera. They tend to have stout bodies and antennae ending in a curved hook. Some rest in a highly characteristic pose, with their hindwings held flat and their forewings held vertically. Most are a dull brownish colour, with varying degrees of white spots on the wings. Many occupy a favoured perch, but they tend to be nervous butterflies and take to the wing rapidly and erratically upon being approached. However, they usually return to the same spot shortly afterwards. Some species are crepuscular (fly at dawn and dusk). The larvae are unusual in that they are smooth with a distinct neck and large head, and because they live inside shelters made by weaving leaves of the food plant together with silk.

Subfamily COELIADINAE
COELIADES
Senegal blue policeman *C. aeschylus* (1205)[G]
*Striped policeman *C. forestan forestan* (1207)[G,N,NW,B]

Subfamily PYRGINAE
TAGIADES
*Clouded flat *T. flesus* (1232)[G,N,NW,B]

SARANGESA
*Grey elfin *S. laelius* (1245)[G,NW,B]

*Orange elfin *S. phidyle* (1246)[G,NW]
Tricerate elfin *S. tricerata tricerata* (1249)[G]

SPIALIA
*Common grizzled skipper *S. spio* (1265)[G,N,NW,B]
Diomus grizzled skipper *S. diomus diomus* (1267)[G,NW,B]
Dromus grizzled skipper *S. dromus* (1268)[G,N,NW,B]

GOMALIA
*Mallow skipper *G. elma elma* (1270)[G,NW]

Subfamily HESPERIINAE
ASTICTOPTERUS
Abject hopper *A. abjecta* (1277)

PROSOPALPUS
Widespread dwarf skipper *P. styla* (1279)[G,NW]

PAROSMODES
Morant skipper *P. morantii axis* (1320)[G]

ACLEROS
Plötz's dusky dart *A. ploetzi* (1341)[G]

ANDRONYMUS
*Falcate dart *A. neander neander* (1365)[G,NW]

ZOPHOPETES
Common palm nightfighter *Z. cerymica* (1374)[G,N]
Western palm nightfighter *Z. quaternata* (1376)[G,NW]

GRETNA
*Common crepuscular skipper *G. waga* (1381)[G,N,NW,B]

PLATYLESCHES
Black hopper *P. galesa* (1432)[G,NW]
*Common hopper *P. moritili* (1434)[N,NW]
Banded hopper *P. picanini* (1438)[NW]
Affinity hopper *P. affinissima* (1439)[G,NW]
'Batanga' hopper *P. batangae* (see comments in Larsen, 2005: 1441)[G]

PELOPIDAS
*Lesser millet skipper *P. mathias* (1444)[G,N,NW,B]
~*Millet skipper *P. thrax* (1445)[unpublished records from Basse by Jon Baker (2008)]

BORBO
False swift *B. fallax* (1446)[NW]
Twin-spot swift *B. fanta* (1447)[G]
Small swift *B. perobscura* (1448)[G]
Marsh swift *B. micans* (1449)[G]
*Olive-haired swift *B. borbonica borbonica* (1450)[G,NW]
*Twin swift *B. gemella* (1451)[G,N,NW,B]
Foolish swift *B. fatuellus fatuellus* (1453)[G,NW]

PARNARA
*Water watchman *Parnara monasi* (1456)[G]

GEGENES
Pigmy skipper *G. 'pumilio' gambica* (1457)[G]
Plain hottentot skipper *G. niso brevicornis* (1459)[G]
*Hottentot skipper *G. hottentota* (1460)

ADDITIONAL DATA FOR NEW SPECIES RECORDS

Small fig blue *M. subornata subornata* (355)
Kerr Serign, Western Division, on garden plant in compound. Dec 2008.
13°26'12"N, 16°43'08"W (only known Gambian record)
Scintillating sapphire *I. scintillans* (414)
Kerr Serign, Western Division, on garden plant in compound. Nov 2008.
13°26'12"N, 16°43'08"W (subsequently found elsewhere)
Light ciliate blue *A. liodes liodes* (512)
Bijilo Forest, Western Division. Jul 2008.
13°6'13"N, 13°43'32"W (only known Gambian record)
Desert babul blue *A. ubaldus* (627)
Kotu, Western Division, roadside scrubland. Dec 2007.
13°27'15"N, 16°42'40"W (subsequently found elsewhere)
Millet skipper *P. thrax* (1445)
Kerr Serign, Western Division, in compound. Dec 2008/Jan 2009.
13°26'12"N, 16°43'08"W (first recorded in Basse by Jon Baker (unpublished
    2008) and subsequently found elsewhere)

NOTES ON SEASONALITY

Some butterfly species are abundant throughout the whole year. Particularly notable in this respect are: Citrus swallowtail *Papilio demodocus demodocus,* White lady *Graphium angolanus baronis,* African emigrant *Catopsilia florella,* Small grass yellow *Eurema brigitta brigitta,* Common dotted border *Mylothris chloris chloris,* Common hairstreak *Hypolycaena philippus philippus,* African grass blue *Zizeeria knysna,* Dark grass blue *Zizina antanossa,* Common tiger *Danaus chrysippus chrysippus* and Dark blue pansy *Junonia oenone oenone.* However, some are distinctly seasonal. For example, Zebra white *Pinacopteryx eriphia tritogenia,* Caper white *Belenois aurota* and Common brown playboy *Deudorix antalus* are usually seen only in the dry season, whereas Narrow-banded green swallowtail *Papilio nireus nireus,* Leaden ciliate blue *Anthene amarah,* Common bush blue *Cacyreus lingeus,* Untailed blue giant cupid *Lepidochrysops synchrematiza,* African babul blue *Azanus jesous,* Common evening brown *Melanitis leda,* Bush charaxes *Charaxes achaemenes atlantica,* Golden pansy *Junonia chorimene,* Soldier pansy *J. terea terea,* Elegant acraea *Acraea egina egina,* Pink acraea *A. caecilia caecilia,* Striped policeman *Coeliades forestan forestan,* Olive-haired swift *Borbo borbonica borbonica* and Twin swift *B. gemella* are common throughout the rains. It should be noted that in some years a certain species may be particularly abundant, whereas in others it may rarely be encountered.

Several migratory species usually appear at the same time each year, although some years are more spectacular than others. For example, the first Painted lady *Vanessa cardui* butterflies usually arrive during September, although this cannot be guaranteed. More reliable are the vast clouds of Caper white *Belenois aurota* butterflies that usually arrive shortly after the rains in October and November. Another strongly migratory species is the African emigrant *Catopsilia florella,* but this is present in The Gambia all year, although migrations increase the numbers significantly. Some species exhibit seasonal dimorphism, with individuals usually smaller and with less distinct markings during the dry season. This is particularly true of many of the blues (family Lycaenidae). A striking example of seasonal dimorphism is to be found in the Darker commodore *Precis antilope*, which looks totally different, with larger dry season forms that have a more falcate forewing shape and with the hindwing drawn out to a point. November and December are probably the best months to see butterflies and visual observation (i.e., without using a butterfly net) counts of greater than 60 species (one third of the Gambian fauna) are easy to attain without the need to travel inland.

LITERATURE & ACKNOWLEDGEMENTS

Barnett, L., Emms, C. & Newport, M. 2003. *Common Butterflies of The Gambia.* Makasutu Wildlife Trust, Serrekunda, The Gambia.

Condamin, M. ca. 1986. *The Butterflies of Senegambia.* Unpublished manuscript.

Gillies, M.T. 1982. Notes on the skippers (Hesperiidae; Lepidoptera) of The Gambia. *Bulletin de l'Institut fondamental d'Afrique Noire, ser. A,* **44**: 160–171.

Larsen, T.B. 2005. *Butterflies of West Africa.* Apollo Books, Stenstrup.

Larsen, T.B. 2008. Forest butterflies in West Africa have resisted extinction... so far (Lepidoptera: Papilionoidea and Hesperioidea). *Biodiversity & Conservation,* **17**: 2833–2847.

Newport, M. 1993. The other end of Africa. *Metamorphosis,* **4**: 165–172.

Newport, M. 1998. *The butterflies of the Kombo Districts of The Gambia: an annotated checklist.* Privately printed document.

Penney, D. 2009. *Field Guide to Wildlife of The Gambia: an introduction to common flowers and animals.* Siri Scientific Press, Manchester.

The author is particularly grateful to the following in The Gambia for their hospitality, advice and discussion: all staff of Bijilo Forest, Abuko Nature Reserve, Tanji Bird Reserve and the Department of Forestry, especially Jato Sillah (director of the DoF), Lamin Bojang, Kebba Sonko and Sulayman Jobe (manager of Bijilo Forest), Alpha Jallow (director of the Department of Parks and Wildlife Management), Clive Barlow, Jon Baker and Luc 'Nouroudine' Paziaud (Gambian Reptiles Farm). I am extremely grateful to Dmitri Logunov and Phil Rispin (Manchester Museum, UK) for help with their extensive collection during the preparation of this book and for providing photographs of pinned material. Torben B. Larsen, Mike Newport and Linda Barnett (UK) are thanked for additional photos. Jon Baker (UK/The Gambia) is thanked for proof reading. I am indebted to Torben B. Larsen, Mike Newport and Jon Baker for assistance, encouragement, tuition and comments on the final draft. Jon Baker, Clive Barlow and Lambert Smith (South Africa) are thanked for providing photos of specimens in the field. All other such photos by the author.

Family PAPILIONIDAE Latreille, 1802

Citrus swallowtail
Papilio demodocus demodocus
Esper, 1798 (13)
Wingspan 100 mm, very common
all year round, sexes similar. An
unmistakable species. Underside
sometimes appears bright orange
due to being covered with pollen.
Larvae often found on citrus
trees. In the early stages the larva
resembles a bird dropping.

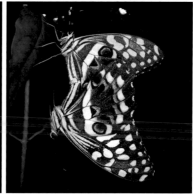

Early stage larva

Late stage larva

Narrow-banded green swallowtail
Papilio nireus nireus Linné, 1758 (11)
Wingspan 110 mm, an unmistakable
species, although the width and colour of
the bands can be variable, sexes similar.
It often appears as a large black butterfly
when in flight and rarely settles for long.
Unlikely to be seen in large numbers, but
common in various habitat types. Larvae
feed on various Rutaceae.

Veined swallowtail
Graphium leonidas leonidas
Fabricius, 1793 (29)
Wingspan 90 mm, sexes similar,
reasonably common in various habitat
types.

White lady swallowtail
Graphium angolanus baronis
Ungemach, 1932 (20)
Wingspan 80 mm, common in
various habitat types. Highly
distinctive, colourful underside.

Family PIERIDAE Swainson, 1820

African emigrant
Catopsilia florella
Fabricius, 1775 (36)
Wingspan 70 mm, very common in various habitats, but not full canopy forest. Male white, female white, creamy white or yellow (the last more often seen during migrations, which may consist of millions of individuals). Larvae usually feed on *Cassia*.

Small grass yellow *Eurema brigitta brigitta* Stoll, 1780 (43)
Wingspan 35 mm, black markings reduced in dry season forms. Often flies with the common grass yellow with which it can be confused.

Courtesy of Lambert Smith

Common grass yellow
Eurema hecabe solifera Butler, 1875
(39)
Wingspan 40 mm, a very common, but
variable species. Underside with a slight
dusting of black scales and sometimes
with a brown apical mark. There is a
distinct notch on the inner margin of the
forewing black tip (even visible from the
underside). Larvae feed on a wide range
of foodplants, particularly Fabaceae.

Zebra white *Pinacopteryx eriphia tritogenia* Klug, 1829 (44)
Wingspan 45 mm, more common in the dry season, sexes similar. Ground
colour varies from white to cream. An unmistakable species.

Courtesy of Jon Baker

Large vagrant
Nepheronia argia argia
Fabricius, 1775 (45)
Wingspan 76 mm, apparently recorded from the area around Pirang forest, this species is easily differentiated from the following one by the presence of a dark apical patch on the underside of the male forewing. Larvae feed on Capparaceae and Celastraceae.

Courtesy of Manchester Museum

Blue vagrant *Nepheronia thalassina thalassina*
Boisduval, 1836 (46)
Wingspan 68 mm, its status in The Gambia is unclear, with no confirmed records for several years, although as a migratory species it may occur sporadically.

Courtesy of Manchester Museum

Small salmon arab NOT ILLUSTRATED
Colotis amata calais Cramer, 1775 (51)
Veined golden arab NOT ILLUSTRATED
Colotis vesta amelia Lucas, 1852 (54)
Both species are medium-sized with black markings on a white and
salmon-pink ground colour (more pronounced in the former). They are
butterflies of the Sahel and Sudanian Savannah, so are more likely to be
seen north of the river.

Purple tip *Colotis ione* Godart, 1819 (58)
Wingspan 56 mm, the largest of the genus and a species of the Sudanian
Savannah. The female can be highly variable, larvae feed on Capparaceae.

Courtesy of Mike Newport

Scarlet tip *Colotis danae eupompe* Klug, 1829 (60)
Wingspan 46 mm, widespread and fairly common, but not seen in large
numbers. The scarlet tip to the forewing may be absent in some females.

Magenta tip NOT ILLUSTRATED
C. celimene sudanicus Aurivillius, 1905 (57)
Wingspan 48 mm, a butterfly of the Sudanian Savannah, with the only
Gambian record originating from a photograph identified by Mike
Newport.

Sulphur orange tip NOT ILLUSTRATED
Colotis aurora evarne Klug, 1829 (61)
Wingspan 44 mm, similar in appearance to the following species, but
smaller with a light yellowish ground colour and paler orange markings.

Large orange tip *Colotis antevippe antevippe* Boisduval, 1836 (62)
Wingspan 53 mm, widespread, common and variable, with the first
specimens usually appearing shortly after the rainy season. Often flies
with the Tiny orange tip *C. evagore antigone* from which it can usually be
differentiated by its larger size, although both species are highly variable in
both size and markings.

Tiny orange tip
Colotis evagore antigone
Boisduval, 1836 (65)
Wingspan 34 mm, widespread, common and variable, with the first specimens usually appearing shortly after the rainy season. Often flies with the Large orange tip, from which it can usually be differentiated by its smaller size, although both species are highly variable in both size and markings.

Caper white *Belenois aurota* Fabricius, 1793 (68)
Wingspan 56 mm, also known as the brown-veined white on account of the markings on the underside of the hindwing. It is a strong migrant and often occurs in huge numbers shortly after the onset of the dry season. This is one of the few butterfly species to be attracted to lights at night.

34

African caper white *Belenois creona creona* Cramer, 1776 (69)
Wingspan 56 mm, this migratory species is common in various habitats throughout the year, but particularly so during the dry season. It is often difficult to differentiate from the previous species when both are on the wing, but is easy to do so when settled.

Pointed caper white *Belenois gidica gidica* Godart, 1819 (70)
Wingspan 60 mm, slightly larger and less common than the preceding *Belenois* species, with more irregular submarginal markings and distinctly pointed forewings. This is primarily a butterfly of the Sudanian Savannah and the Sahel.

Calypso caper white *Belenois calypso calypso* Drury, 1773 (73)
Wingspan 65 mm, primarily a forest species and the largest of the Gambian *Belenois*. It is common in Guinean Savannah, particularly in forest gaps, e.g., in Abuko Forest and Pirang, but not so frequent by the coast, although it does occur in Bijilo Forest from time to time. Females are rather variable.

Creamy small white *Dixeia orbona orbona* Geyer, 1832 [1837] (79)
Wingspan 45 mm, an extremely common small white butterfly, the male is usually brilliant white with thin black marginal markings and the female is a dirty white, often with a yellowish underside. Common in forests and at forest edges.

36

African albatross *Appias epaphia epaphia* Cramer, 1779 (87)
Wingspan 52 mm, male similar in appearance to that of the Creamy
small white *Dixeia orbona orbona*, female with more extensive dark
markings, including a thick marginal band on the border of the hindwing.
The **Common Albatross** *A. sylvia sylvia* Fabricius, 1775 (84) [NOT
ILLUSTRATED] is also recorded from The Gambia, with records from
Pirang during August and October by Newport (1998).

Desert white NOT ILLUSTRATED
Pontia glauconome Klug, 1829 (83)
A desert adapted butterfly not usually found as far south as The Gambia.

African spirit *Leptosia alcesta
alcesta* Stoll, 1781 (88)
Wingspan 40 mm, a small species, with a
highly characteristic lazy, slow flapping
flight close to the forest floor, usually in
shaded areas. The wings are rounded,
with a black apical patch on the forewing
and a large black subapical spot (visible
in the photo), which is sometimes much
reduced in females. These markings can
be difficult to detect in flight.

Common dotted border *Mylothris chloris chloris*
Fabricius, 1775 (95)
Wingspan, 63 mm, an unmistakable species, having an orange hindwing with a thick black border occupying more than half the wing in females. They have a slower, more relaxed flight than other whites of similar size and are common in various habitats throughout the year, particularly towards the end of the rainy season. Larvae feed on Loranthaceae.

Family LYCAENIDAE Leach, 1815

Common woolly legs *Lachnocnema emperamus*
Snellen, 1872 (133)
Wingspan 28 mm, their legs are covered with hairs (as their name suggests), which have been proposed to function as a defensive mechanism against ant attacks. The sexes are similar, although the male can vary in both ground colour and size. The specimen in the photos was found perched on vegetation at the margin of a rice field.

African apefly NOT ILLUSTRATED
Spalgis lemolea pilos Druce, 1890 (130)
Wingspan 32 mm, an unmistakable chalk-white species with distinct
black bands on the forewing costa and margin, and also on the costa of the
hindwing. Generally a butterfly of forests and forest edges, but also found
elsewhere, although not particularly common. The sexes are similar.

Roche's epitola NOT ILLUSTRATED
Cephetola subcoerulea Roche, 1954 (300)
The original Gambian record from Banjul may be an error (Larsen, 2005).

Common fig blue *Myrina silenus silenus* Fabricius, 1807 (354)
Wingspan 36 mm, an unmistakable species. Sexes similar, with extremely
long tails and royal blue, black and chestnut wings. Common on figs and
also seems to be attracted to the coral tree *Erythrina senegalensis.*

Small fig blue *Myrina subornata
subornata* Lathy, 1903 (355)
Wingspan 32 mm, slightly smaller than
the above species, lacking the chestnut
wing tips and with shorter, but very
distinct tails. Sexes similar, with dark,
royal blue uppersides. A relatively rare
African butterfly. This new record for
The Gambia was found in a private
compound in Kerr Serign.

Common silver spot *Aphnaeus orcas* Drury, 1782 (361)
Wingspan 36 mm, the female upperside is uniformly brown and the
underside is lighter than, but similar to the male. Both sexes are variable,
but should not easily be confused with any other species. At forest edges
and in clearings.

Courtesy of Manchester Museum

Saharan silverline NOT ILLUSTRATED
Apharitis nilus Hewitson, 1865 (368)
Wingspan 32 mm, primarily a butterfly of the Sahel, but occasionally
found further south, particularly in Sudanian Savannah, so more likely to
be seen north of the river.

Common silverline *Spindasis mozambica* Bertolini, 1850 (369)
Wingspan 32 mm, a variable, but unmistakble species within The
Gambia. Sexes similar, but the male has more pointed wings. This is
primarily a Guinean Savannah species, which is not often encountered.

Courtesy of Manchester Museum

Western virgin NOT ILLUSTRATED
Dapidodigma hymen Fabricius, 1775 (359)
This is not a common butterfly, with only one Gambian record from Pirang
by Newport (1998).

Common scarlet *Axiocerces harpax* Fabricius, 1775 (375)
Wingspan 34 mm, a common, unmistakable species (within The Gambia).
As with many other species, the markings are often much reduced in dry
season forms. They are often seen perching on *Neocarya*. They fly rapidly
and erratically when disturbed and can be difficult to follow with the eye.

Blue savannah sapphire *Iolaus menas menas* Druce, 1890 (393)
Wingspan 40 mm, both sexes with black wing tips on upperside, male sky
blue, female white suffused with blue at wing bases; undersides similar.
Often perch high in trees, especially those with parasitic west African
mistletoe (*Tapinanthus*) on which the larvae feed. Reasonably common.

Courtesy of Torben B Larsen

Iasis sapphire *Iolaus iasis iasis* Hewitson, 1865 (436)
Wingspan 36 mm, both sexes similar to the other species illustrated, but the forewing underside usually has two fine black lines running parallel with the margin. On the hindwing underside, the orange crown on the upper spot is not well developed. There is also a fine red submarginal line along the distal base of the hindwing to the tornal eyespot. In contrast to the other species illustrated, the blue of the female forewing upperside also runs along the posterior margin of the forewing.

Scintillating sapphire *Iolaus scintillans* Aurivillius, 1905 (414)
Wingspan 36 mm, both sexes similar to the above species, but the upper spot on the hindwing is not surrounded by orange and there is an orange streak between the fine submarginal line and the edge of the wing. Also, the base of the forewing underside costa is usually (but not always) red.

Druce's sapphire NOT ILLUSTRATED
Iolaus lukabas Druce, 1890 (403)
Wingspan 43 mm, both sexes blue with black wing tips on the upperside, and with a distinct orange-brown submarginal line running parallel to the edge of the hindwing. Uncommon.

Large green sapphire NOT ILLUSTRATED
Iolaus calisto Westwood, 1851 (407)
Wingspan 40 mm, upperside of both sexes with typical *Iolaus* pattern, but male dark brown and emerald green, female dark brown and dirty white suffused with blue. Underside similar to *Iolaus menas menas*. Uncommon.

Common brown playboy *Deudorix antalus* Hopffer, 1855 (494)
Wingspan 35 mm, sexes similar. This is a very common butterfly, often seen perching on *Icacina oliviformis* in open waste land, but also occurs frequently in many other habitat types. Three other species [NOT ILLUSTRATED]: **Pomegranate playboy** *D. livia* Klug, 1834 (495), **Coffee playboy** *D. lorisona abriana* Libert, 2004 (496) and the **Apricot playboy** *D. dinochares* Grose-Smith, 1887 (498), the males of which have black and red/orange uppersides, have also been recorded from The Gambia, although they are seldom seen.

Green-streaked playboy NOT ILLUSTRATED
Pilodeudorix diyllus occidentalis Libert, 2004 (458)
Blue heart playboy NOT ILLUSTRATED
Pilodeudorix caerulea caerulea Druce, 1890 (460)
Both species are medium-sized (wingspan 30 mm) with shiny, dark blue males and drab females. Forewings have black tips. Both are uncommon.

Common hairstreak *Hypolycaena philippus philippus*
Fabricius, 1793 (443)
Wingspan 32 mm, a very common and unmistakable species found in a
wide variety of different habitat types. Female upperside dark brown with
two rows of white lunules close to the tornal spots, the upper of which
has an orange crown. Males have a violet sheen, fly rapidly, are extremely
territorial and are often seen chasing away competitors. Larvae feed on a
wide variety of different plants.

Red-spot ciliate blue NOT ILLUSTRATED
Anthene lunulata Trimen, 1894 (517)
Wingspan 32 mm, similar to the Leaden ciliate blue *Anthene amarah*,
but with only three black dots (excluding tornal spots) on the hindwing
underside; two on the dorsal margin. The orange of the tornal spot is well
develped on the upperside in both sexes. The only published Gambian
record is an Abuko sighting reported in Newport (1998).

Nigerian ciliate blue NOT ILLUSTRATED
Triclema nigeriae Aurivillius, 1905 (556)
African line blue NOT ILLUSTRATED
Pseudonacaduba sichela sichela Wallengren, 1857 (565)
Two small, rather non-descript species that are rarely encountered, the
latter with only one Gambian record (Pirang) reported in Newport (1998).

Leaden ciliate blue *Anthene amarah* Guérin-Méneville, 1847 (516)
Wingspan 25 mm, the male is a light, glossy leadish colour. A reasonably
common species at certain times of the year, from the early rains until
well into the dry season. Found in open, dry areas.

Common ciliate blue *Anthene larydas* Cramer, 1780 (523)
Wingspan 28 mm, a common forest butterfly, often seen sunning itself in
gaps and at forest edges. The female is dark brown. **Crawshay's ciliate
blue** *A. crawshayi crawshayi* Butler, 1899 (524) [NOT ILLUSTRATED]
is very similar to this species, but slightly smaller and lighter in colour.

Light ciliate blue (512)

Anthene liodes liodes Hewitson, 1874
Wingspan 28 mm, an unmistakable
species when viewed from the
underside. The upperside of the male
is violet, whereas that of the female is
a brownish colour suffused with blue.
In forest gaps and at forest edges. Not
particularly common. This photo taken
in Bijilo Forest represents the first
record of this species in The Gambia.

Common zebra blue *Leptotes pirithous* Linné, 1767 (578)

Wingspan 30 mm, a common species during the dry season. Correct
identification from other practially identical species, including **Babault's
zebra blue** *L. babaulti* Stempffer, 1935 (579) (known from The Gambia:
NOT ILLUSTRATED) requires microscopic examination of the genitalia.

Courtesy of Jon Baker

Courtesy of Jon Baker

Pea blue *Lampides boeticus*
Linné, 1767 (567)
Wingspan 34 mm, an unmistakable
butterfly with a highly distinctive
underside. The upperside of
the male is a uniform violet. A
strongly migratory species, which
also occurs in other parts of the
world (including sometimes in the
UK). It is reasonably common in
open areas.

Common bush blue *Cacyreus lingeus* Stoll, 1782 (575)
Wingspan 30 mm, with short tails and a highly distinctive underside. Very
common on flowers (particularly *Hoslundia opposita*) in forest clearings
during the rainy season, but persists until well into the dry season. There
are two other species in West Africa that are practically identical.

Savannah pied pierrot
Tuxentius cretosus nodieri
Oberthür, 1883 (583)
Wingspan 30 mm, an unmistakable species, common during the rains and into the dry season. Easily distinguished from the closely related *Tarucus* by the large white area on the hindwing underside. It is usually seen fluttering around the Chinese date plant *Zizyphus mauritiana*. Sexes similar.

Ungemach's pierrot *Tarucus ungemachi* Stempffer, 1942 (586)
Wingspan 25 mm, a common species usually seen fluttering around the Chinese date plant *Zizyphus mauritiana*. Note that the second inner band along the forewing margin forms a row of broken blotches.

African pierrot
Tarucus theophrastus Fabricius, 1759 (587)
Wingspan 23 mm, practically identical to the above species, but in the former the wings of the male are more rounded.

Mediterranean pierrot *Tarucus rosacea* Austaut, 1885 (588)
Wingspan 23 mm, a common species usually seen fluttering around the
Chinese date plant *Zizyphus mauritiana*. The second inner band along the
forewing margin forms an unbroken line, whereas it tends to be broken in
the aforementioned species.

White-tipped cupid
Eicochrysops hippocrates
Fabricius, 1793 (593)
Wingspan 25 mm, a small, tailed
butterfly, with white wing tips in
the male and unmistakable in this
respect. Distributed throughout
Africa.

African cupid *Euchrysops osiris*
Hopffer, 1855 (604)
Wingspan 30 mm, easily identified
from other Gambian *Euchrysops* by
the presence of tails in both sexes.
Male with violet upperside, whereas
that of the female is more blue with
darker forewing margins. Both sexes
have two orange-crowned, black
tornal spots.

Smoky bean cupid *Euchrysops malathana* Boisduval, 1833 (601)
Wingspan 30 mm, common in various habitats during the early dry
season. Male with brownish-grey upperside. The slightly smaller **Milky
bean cupid** *E. nilotica* Aurivillius, 1904 (602) **[NOT ILLUSTRATED]** is
similar.

Untailed blue giant cupid
Lepidochrysops synchrematiza
Bethune-Baker, 1923 (611)
Wingspan 45 mm, the large size and
distinct underside markings make this
species readily identifiable within The
Gambia. It is common in forest gaps
during the early rainy season. The
upperside of the male is violet, slightly
less so in the female. Female has a
black tornal spot crowned with orange.

Desert babul blue *Azanus ubaldus*
Cramer, 1782 (627)
Wingspan 23 mm, a butterfly of the
drier zones, this is the first record of
the species for The Gambia. It can
be common in the dry season, but is
easily overlooked due to its small size.
Upperside of male violet-blue, that of
the female brown.

African babul blue *Azanus jesous*
Guérin-Méneville, 1847 (628)
Wingspan 25 mm, the markings are
more strongly defined than in the
preceding species. The **Black-bordered
babul blue** *A. moriqua* Wallengren, 1857
(629) [NOT ILLUSTRATED] is similar
but the underside has a grey-white (not
brownish) ground colour.

Sky-blue cupid *Chilades eleusis* Demaison, 1888 (633)
Wingspan 22 mm, a beautiful butterfly, the male has a stunning, almost
sparkling, light blue upperside (unmistakable in this respect), the female is
rather drab dark brown. In open, dry habitats, usually at ground level. Dry
season forms may be smaller and without a well defined underside pattern.

Grass Jewel *Chilades trochylus*
Freyer, 1843 (634)
Wingspan 20 mm, easily identified by
the presence of three tornal spots, all
crowned with orange and visible on
both the upperside and underside of
the hindwing in both sexes. Upperside
brown, sexes similar. In open areas
during the dry season, but easily
overlooked.

African grass blue *Zizeeria knysna* Trimen, 1862 (635)
Wingspan 23 mm, ubiquitous in open areas throughout the year, usually staying at ground level. This is certainly the most common Gambian butterfly. The underside markings differ from the following species, but are sometimes absent in dry season forms. Female upperside brown.

Dark grass blue *Zizina antanossa* Mabille, 1877 (636)
Wingspan 25 mm, flies in open habitats with the above species, which makes them impossible to identify accurately on the wing. However, the arrangement of spots on the hindwing underside (they don't form a smooth curve) makes for easy identification when at rest.

Tiny grass blue NOT ILLUSTRATED
Zizula hylax Fabricius, 1775 (637)
Wingspan 23 mm, similar to the above two species, but smaller with better defined underside markings and an additional spot along the anterior edge of the forewing.

Family NYMPHALIDAE Swainson, 1827

African tiger *Danaus chrysippus chrysippus* Linné, 1758 (647)
Wingspan 83 mm, one of the most common of the large Gambian
butterflies, found in all open habitats throughout the year. These butterflies
are supposedly distasteful to predators and serve as a model for females
of *Hypolimnas misippus* (Nymphalidae) which mimic it, and with which
it may be confused. However, the hindwings of the mimic are often (but
not always) a similar orange colour to the forewings, whereas those of the
Gambian race of the African tiger are white.

Small monk NOT ILLUSTRATED
Amauris damocles damocles Fabricius, 1793 (653)
Previously recorded from The Gambia, but the record has been questioned
by some experts, although the species is known to occur in southern
Senegal.

Common evening brown *Melanitis leda* Linné, 1758 (658)
Wingspan 73 mm, a large, common species in various habitats.
Underside highly variable with season. They fly rapidly, mainly at dusk.
When disturbed during the day they fly off a short distance into nearby
vegetation. This species is similar to the next and can be best differentiated
by the relative postions of the white spots on the forewing. In *M. leda* the
lower spot is immediately below the upper, whereas in *M. libya* they are
offset. They are also surrounded by red, which tends not to be the case in
M. libya. Sexes similar, larvae feed on grasses.

Courtesy of Manchester Museum

Courtesy of Clive Barlow

Violet-eyed evening brown *Melanitis libya* Distant, 1882 (659)
Wingspan 73 mm, extremely similar to *M. leda*, from which it can be
differentiated as described above. However, it is less common.

Courtesy of Manchester Museum

Swamp ringlet NOT ILLUSTRATED
Ypthimomorpha itonia Hewitson, 1865 (724)
Wingspan 32 mm, hindwing underside with seven submarginal eyespots.

Vulgar bush brown *Bicyclus vulgaris* Butler, 1868 (690)
Wingspan 42 mm, dull brown upperside. Eyespots on the underside do not
show through on the forewing as in *Ypthima*. They are rarely seen unless
using baited butterfly traps. Other often confusingly similar Gambian
species [NOT ILLUSTRATED]: **Western large bush brown** *B. zinebi*
Butler, 1869 (673), **Rock bush brown** *B. pavonis* Butler, 1876 (679),
Lesser rock bush brown *B. milyas* Hewitson, 1864 (680), **Dark vulgar
bush brown** *B. sandace* Hewitson, 1877 (692), **Angular bush brown** *B.
angulosus angulosus* Butler, 1868 (698), **Common savannah bush brown**
B. safitza safitza Hewitson, 1851 (701), **Funereal bush brown** *B. funebris*
Guérin-Méneville, 1844 (702).

Common three-ring *Ypthima asterope asterope* Klug, 1832 (715)
Wingspan 30 mm, similar to the two other Gambian species [NOT
ILLUSTRATED]: **Condamin's three-ring** *Y. condamini nigeriae*
Kielland, 1982 (716) and **Vuattoux's ringlet** *Y. vuattouxi* Kielland,
1982 (718). They usually fly close to the ground and all are variable,
individually as well as seasonally and so are difficult to identify with
certainty without microscopic examination of the genitalia.

Pearl charaxes (725)

Charaxes varanes vologeses Mabille, 1876
Wingspan 90 mm, the most common of
the Gambian charaxes, present in various
habitats throughout the year. These are fast
and high fliers that are usually seen as solitary
individuals. They rarely settle with their wings
open, although the territorial males will often
perch high up in foliage with the wings held
slightly apart. At rest, the underside resembles a
dead leaf. The sexes are similar.

Green-veined charaxes *Charaxes candiope candiope*
Godart, 1824 (728)

Wingspan 87 mm, in various habitats, but not common in West Africa in
general (Gambian status unclear). The underside can be variable, but the
green veins of the forewing can usually be seen in the field. The female is
larger than the male and has slightly longer tails. Larvae feed on *Croton*.

Courtesy of Manchester Museum   Courtesy of Manchester Museum

56

Bamboo charaxes *Charaxes boueti* Feisthamel, 1850 (730)
Wingspan 78 mm, female is larger, but with a darker ground colour and a
broad yellowish postdiscal band. Larvae feed on bamboo.

Courtesy of Torben B Larsen   Courtesy of Mike Newport

Cream-bordered charaxes *Charaxes epijasius* Reiche, 1850 (734)
Wingspan 98 mm, a highly distinctive butterfly, which is often seen in
coastal scrub areas, exhibiting its characteristic gliding flight, sometimes
close to the ground. Found in both Guinean and Sudanian Savannah.
Sexes similar in appearance, larvae feed on a variety of different plants.

Courtesy of Jon Baker

Giant charaxes *Charaxes castor castor* Cramer, 1775 (736)
Wingspan 105 mm, a large and powerful butterfly, which occurs in a wide
range of habitats, although it is rarely encountered in The Gambia. Sexes
similar in appearance, larvae feed on a variety of different plants.

Courtesy of Manchester Museum

Bush charaxes

Charaxes achaemenes atlantica
van Someren, 1970 (755)
Wingspan 83 mm, one of the
most common charaxes. The
upperside has a white band
crossing all four wings, also visible
on the underside. Sexes similar
in appearance, larvae feed on a
variety of different plants.

Courtesy of Jon Baker

Courtesy of Mike Newport

Flame-bordered charaxes NOT ILLUSTRATED
Charaxes protoclea protoclea Feisthamel, 1850 (729)
This is a widespread species that has been previously recorded from The
Gambia, although its current status is considered uncertain.

Savannah demon charaxes *Charaxes viola viola*
van Someren, 1970 (770)
Wingspan 64 mm, one of the smaller and more common charaxes, found
in various habitat types. The upperside of the male is very dark (almost
black) with a few small blue spots close to the anterior margin of the
forewing. Larvae feed on a variety of different plants including *Acacia*.

Painted lady

Vanessa cardui cardui Linné, 1758 (791)

Wingspan 63 mm, specimens arrive in The Gambia as migrants from North Africa, usually around September or October. They can often be seen sunning themselves in open areas, but when disturbed fly very quickly and erratically, remaining close to the ground and are very difficult to follow with the eye. Sexes similar in appearance, larvae feed on a variety of different plants.

Darker commodore

Precis antilope Feisthamel, 1850 (793)

Wingspan 51 mm, with two distinct morphs, the dry season one being the largest. Wet season forms have more rounded wings and the red ground colour is reduced to a golden yellow. Sexes similar in appearance, larvae feed on Lamiaceae. Widespread in The Gambia but not usually encountered with great frequency, nor in large numbers.

Diadem *Hypolimnas misippus* Linné, 1764 (801)

Wingspan 75 mm, with pronounced sexual dimorphism. The female (top photos) is a mimic of the African tiger *Danaus chrysippus chrysippus* (Nymphalidae), which is thought to be distasteful to predators. Thus, this butterfly escapes predation without having to invest in energetically costly chemical defences. In order for such mimicry to work, the mimic needs to be less common than the model, creating a constraint on the population size of the mimic. This species offsets this limitation by having only the female as the mimic. The male tends to be more nervous and a faster flier than the female, a behaviour which has presumably evolved because it does not appear to be distasteful to predators. The female is polymorphic, some specimens having white hindwings and some with orange. In some females the forewings lack the black and white apical markings and appear mainly orange. Most common during the rainy season. Larvae feed on a variety of different plants.

61

Variable eggfly
Hypolimnas anthedon anthedon
Doubleday, 1845 (802)
Wingspan 84 mm, uncommon in The
Gambia and sitings possibly represent
strays from Cassamance. Different
morphs mimic different *Amauris*
species. It has a slow, gentle flight and
I have observed it in coastal forests
and gardens. Larvae feed primarily on
Urticaceae.

Blue pansy *Junonia orithya madagascariensis* Guenée, 1865 (813)
Wingspan 50 mm, very beautiful, but not particularly common as it is
primarily a butterfly of the Sudanian Savannah. This species cannot be
confused with any other, the sexes are similar. Sometimes attracted to
lights at night. Larvae feed on a variety of different plants.

Dark blue pansy *Junonia oenone oenone* Linné, 1758 (814)
Wingspan 55 mm, one of The Gambia's most common pansies, reasonably abundant year round in various habitats. Males are extremely territorial and are often seen chasing other butterflies away from their chosen patch. This species cannot be confused with any other, the sexes are similar, but the female is duller and may lack the large blue spots.

Yellow pansy *Junonia hierta cebrene* Trimen, 1870 (815)
Wingspan 51 mm, an unmistakable species with similar sexes, but the blue spots may be absent in the female. Not particularly common, larvae feed on Acanthaceae.

Courtesy of Manchester Museum

63

Little commodore *Junonia sophia sophia* Fabricius, 1793 (819)
Wingspan 49 mm, the smallest member of the genus and one of the most common, especially during the rainy and early dry seasons. Usually found in disturbed habitats and often in large numbers, visiting flowers such as *Tridax*. Rarely seen in dense forest. Sexes similar, larvae feed on Acanthaceae.

Golden pansy *Junonia chorimene* Guérin-Méneville, 1844 (822)
Wingspan 55 mm, a widespread butterfly of open country in both Guinean and Sudanian Savannahs, including farmed land, but also found at forest edges, though not encountered often in The Gambia. Sexes similar and confusion with other species is unlikely. Larvae feed on Acanthaceae.

Soldier pansy *Junonia terea terea* Drury, 1773 (823)
Wingspan 55 mm, a low and weak flier that rarely settles for long. Common towards the end of the rains (in some years) in disturbed forest habitats such as the trail clearings in Abuko. Sexes similar and confusion with other species is unlikely. Larvae feed on Acanthaceae.

Courtesy of Jon Baker

Pirate *Catacroptera cloanthe ligata* Rothschild & Jordan, 1903 (824)
Wingspan 51 mm, a relatively scarce species. This butterfly may be confused with the darker commodore *Precis antilope*, but the pirate hindwing has a full row of black eye spots with sky-blue pupils.

Courtesy of Manchester Museum

African joker *Byblia anvatara crameri* Aurivillius, 1894 (826)
Wingspan 50 mm, an unmistakable species, although not encountered often. The orange colour of the female is not so intense as that of the male (illustrated) and the black markings are not so well defined. The underside pattern may vary between wet and dry season morphs.

Courtesy of Mike Newport

Senegal palm forester *Bebearia senegalensis* Herrich-Schäffer, 1858 (101
Wingspan 66 mm, previously recorded only from Abuko Nature Reserve, but not found for several years and now thought to be locally extinct.

Courtesy of Mike Newport

River sailor *Neptis serena serena* Overlaet, 1955 (905)
Wingspan 52 mm, in dry open forest and often close to water. This is a highly distinctive butterfly, with a graceful characteristic soaring, gliding flight interspersed with the occasional wing beat. It rarely settles for long. Sexes similar. There are many very similar species in West Africa.

Guineafowl *Hamanumida daedalus* Fabricius, 1755 (951)
Wingspan 65 mm, in savannah and open areas. This is a highly distinctive butterfly, usually seen flitting around at ground level and settling with wings outstretched. There is often a male in pursuit of a female. Sexes similar, larvae feed primarily on Combretaceae.

Ceres forester *Euphaedra ceres ceres* Fabricius, 1775 (1083)
Wingspan 74 mm, sexes similar in appearance. Apparently recorded in The Gambia only from Abuko Nature Reserve during 1999.

Courtesy of Linda Barnett

67

Widespread forester *Euphaedra medon pholus*
van der Hoeven, 1840 (1046)
Wingspan 72 mm, the most sexually dimorphic member of the genus and
also probably the most ecologically tolerant. Typically a forest butterfly,
but sometimes also occurs in disturbed areas. It is a very strong and fast
flier. Larvae feed on Sapindaceae.

Courtesy of Mike Newport

Encedon acraea *Acraea encedon encedon* Linné, 1758 (1153)
Wingspan 52 mm, with sexes similar, but variable in both size and colour.
Found in various habitats, the larvae feed on a variety of different plants.

Courtesy of Mike Newport

Encedana acraea NOT ILLUSTRATED
Acraea encedana Pierre, 1976 (1154)
Resembles the above, but slightly larger and with a similar patterning to
the African tiger. Status in The Gambia unclear.

Small orange acraea *Acraea serena serena* Fabricius, 1775 (1159)
Wingspan 42 mm, common from the mid-rainy season, but reaches its highest numbers in the dry season when it can be extremely abundant in various different habitats, but particularly in open areas. Males are often found roosting together. The female can be rather variable.

Bonasia acraea *Acraea bonasia bonasia* Fabricius, 1775 (1165)
Wingspan 45 mm, females usually larger, with a similar pattern to the male illustrated, but not so bold and somewhat more dirty in appearance.

Courtesy of Manchester Museum

Elegant acraea *Acraea egina egina* Cramer, 1775 (1176)
Wingspan 74 mm, a striking butterfly, aptly named. It has an elegant, gliding flight, often high up in forest clearings, although it also settles lower down. The orange patch with a black spot on the forewing upperside serves to identify it from similar species. The female is usually rather drab and at a distance on the wing could be mistaken for the Abadima acraea *A. pseudegina*.

Large spotted acraea *Acraea zetes zetes* Linné, 1758 (1180)
Wingspan 74 mm, most easily differentiated from similar species in having dark forewing uppersides with a white subapical band and bright orange marginal spots on the forewing underside. Sexes similar.

Abadima acraea *Acraea pseudegina* Westwood, 1852 (1178)
Wingspan 70 mm, most easily differentiated from similar species by the narrow, black margin on the hindwing upperside (distinctly thicker in *A. egina* and *A. zetes*) and the smoky appearance of the forewings. Sexes similar.

Courtesy of Manchester Museum

Pink acraea *Acraea caecilia caecilia* Fabricius, 1781 (1179)
Wingspan 56 mm, often flies low down during the rainy season, visiting patches of *Tridax* flowers, usually in open urban areas. The flight appears rather relaxed. Sexes similar, but females more white than pink.

Common glassy acraea *Acraea quirina quirina* Fabricius, 1781 (1184)
Wingspan 44 mm, the transparent forewings make this an unmistakable
species within The Gambia, where it has been found in Abuko Forest.

Courtesy of Manchester Museum

Wandering donkey NOT ILLUSTRATED
Acraea neobule neobule Doubleday, 1847 (1185)
Large smoky acraea NOT ILLUSTRATED
Acraea camaena Drury, 1773 (1187)
Clouded bematistes NOT ILLUSTRATED
Acraea umbra carpenteri le Doux, 1937 (1190)
None of the above species are particularly common within The Gambia.
For more information on these species see Larsen (2005).

Common leopard fritillary *Phalanta phalantha aethiopica*
Rothschild & Jordan, 1903 (1200)
Wingspan 57 mm, a common, unmistakable species within The Gambia.
Found in many different habitat types, although not often seen in large
numbers. It rarely settles for long. Sexes similar.

Courtesy of Jon Baker

72

Family HESPERIIDAE Latreille, 1809

Striped policeman *Coeliades forestan forestan* Stoll, 1782 (1207)
Wingspan 53 mm, found in many different habitat types. It is most likely
to be seen perched on a leaf during a forest walk. They are easily disturbed
and fly away rapidly upon being approached, returning to the perch a short
time later. Sexes similar. *C. pisistratus* is a similar West African species,
but it has a black bar and two distinct black spots in the white band (not
currently recorded from The Gambia, but possibly occurs there). Larvae
feed on a variety of different plants.

Courtesy of Torben B Larsen

Senegal blue policeman NOT ILLUSTRATED
Coeliades aeschylus Plötz, 1884 (1205)
Wingspan 57 mm, a uniform dark skipper with a bright orange tip to the
hindwing.

Clouded flat *Tagiades flesus* Fabricius, 1781 (1232)
Wingspan 48 mm, the white hindwing underside is clearly evident in
flight. It is a fast flier, but comes to rest relatively quickly, usually on the
underside of a leaf. A common butterfly, most easily seen in forest gaps.

Grey elfin *Sarangesa laelius* Mabille, 1877 (1245)
Wingspan 34 mm, a common, variable and widespread butterfly found in various habitats. It flits around at ground level, coming to rest with wings apart. In contrast to *S. phidyle* the underside is dull with few marks.

Orange elfin *Sarangesa phidyle* Walker, 1870 (1246)
Wingspan 34 mm, similar to the above species, but a lighter brown colour and with the hindwing underside distinctly orange. It flits around at ground level, coming to rest with wings spread apart.

Courtesy of Manchester Museum

Tricerate elfin NOT ILLUSTRATED
Sarangesa tricerata tricerata Mabille, 891 (1249)
Wingspan 32 mm, vaguely similar in general appearance to *S. laelius*, but with a distinct trilobate mark on the forewing upperside and with four (rather than three) subapical spots. Considered a rare butterfly in Africa.

Common grizzled skipper *Spialia spio* Linné, 1767 (1265)
Wingspan 28 mm, a common butterfly found in various habitats. It flits
around at ground level, often visiting flowers such as *Tridax* and *Nelsonia*
or animal dung. This is one of three extremely similar species. The other
two [NOT ILLUSTRATED]: **Diomus grizzled skipper** *S. diomus diomus*
Hopffer, 1855 (1267) and **Dromus grizzled skipper** *S. dromus* Plötz, 1884
(1268) have the white band on the underside of the hindwing entire rather
than broken.

Mallow skipper *Gomalia elma elma* Trimen, 1862 (1270)
Wingspan 30 mm, the distinctly marbled appearance precludes it from
being confused with other diurnal skippers. Not a particularly common
butterfly, the left photograph was taken in an open area of Abuko Nature
Reserve. Sexes similar.

Courtesy of Jon Baker

Falcate dart *Andronymus neander neander* Plötz, 1884 (1365)
Wingspan 40 mm, one of the few migratory skippers, so may appear in large numbers at certain times, then be relatively scarce at others. Within The Gambia it has been recorded from near Fajara by Newport (1998). It is easily recognized by the large white spots on the hindwing. Sexes similar.

Courtesy of Manchester Museum

Abject hopper NOT ILLUSTRATED
Astictopterus abjecta Snellen, 1872 (1277)
Widespread dwarf skipper NOT ILLUSTRATED
Prosopalpus styla Evans, 1937 (1279)
Morant skipper NOT ILLUSTRATED
Parosmodes morantii axis Evans, 1937 (1320)
Plötz's dusky dart NOT ILLUSTRATED
Acleros ploetzi Mabille, 1890 (1341)
Common palm nightfighter NOT ILLUSTRATED
Zophopetes cerymica Hewitson, 1867 (1374)
Western palm nightfighter NOT ILLUSTRATED
Zophopetes quaternata Mabille, 1876 (1376)

Most of the above species are rather dull, non-descript dark brown-black skippers without any striking markings and some are known only from single records. *Zophopetes* are large skippers with a strong and rapid flight, usually seen at dusk.

Common crepuscular skipper *Gretna waga* Plötz, 1886 (1381)
Wingspan 47 mm, a large and common skipper in various habitat types.
They usually fly at dawn and dusk, but will flit around rapidly if disturbed
during the day. Sexes similar, larvae feed on Arecaceae.

Courtesy of Torben B Larsen

Common hopper *Platylesches moritili* Wallengren, 1857 (1434)
Wingspan 31 mm, a relatively common butterfly of open woodland,
most likely to be seen along the coast on *Neocarya macrophylla*. A
particularly good place to see them is along the coastal track in Bijilo
Forest. There are four more similar species recorded from The Gambia
[NOT ILLUSTRATED]: **Black hopper** *P. galesa* Hewitson, 1877 (1432),
Banded hopper *P. picanini* Holland, 1894 (1438), **Affinity hopper** *P.
affinissima* Strand, 1921 (1439), '**Batanga' hopper** *P. batangae* Holland,
1894 (1441). Larvae of all species feed on Chrysobalanaceae.

Lesser millet skipper (1444)
Pelopidas mathias Fabricius, 1798
Wingspan 37 mm, a common species
found in various habitat types and
particularly common in urban areas,
where it often rests on walls. The spots
on the underside of the hindwing may be
very difficult to see in dry season forms.
Larvae feed on Poaceae.

Millet skipper *Pelopidas thrax* Hübner, 1821 (1445)
Wingspan 41 mm, slightly larger than the previous species and with less
well defined markings on the hindwing. Larvae feed on Poaceae. This is
the first documented species record for The Gambia, although this species
was previously found in Basse by Jon Baker (unpublished).

Courtesy of Torben B Larsen

Water watchman (1456)
Parnara monasi Trimen, 1889
Wingspan 32 mm, a small and
relatively scarce species, usually
encountered by swamps and other
wetland habitats.

Courtesy of Jon Baker

Olive-haired swift
Borbo borbonica borbonica
Boisduval, 1833 (1450)
Wingspan 41 mm, the relatively large size, colour and pointed forewings make this species readily identifiable. It is found in various habitats and can be numerous along the coast towards the end of the rainy season. Sexes similar, larvae feed on Poaceae.

Twin swift *Borbo gemella* Mabille, 1884 (1451)
Wingspan 35 mm, one of the most common Gambian skippers. It has three spots on the hindwing underside in a similar arrangement to the above species, but it is smaller and darker brown. Sexes similar, larvae feed on Poaceae.

False swift NOT ILLUSTRATED
Borbo fallax Gaede, 1916 (1446)
Twin-spot swift NOT ILLUSTRATED
Borbo fanta Evans, 1937 (1447)
Small swift NOT ILLUSTRATED
Borbo perobscura Druce, 1912 (1448)
Marsh swift NOT ILLUSTRATED
Borbo micans Holland, 1896 (1449)
Foolish swift NOT ILLUSTRATED
Borbo fatuellus fatuellus Hopffer, 1855 (1453)

Similar to the foregoing members of the genus already illustrated, although *B. micans* has a distinctly orange tint in both sexes.

Hottentot skipper *Gegenes hottentota* Latreille, 1824 (1460) Wingspan 30 mm, not particularly common. The **Pigmy skipper** *G. 'pumilio' gambica* Mabille, 1878 (1457) and **Plain hottentot skipper** *G. niso brevicornis* Plötz, 1884 (1459) [NOT ILLUSTRATED] have also been recorded from The Gambia and are somewhat similar in appearance.

Courtesy of Jon Baker

Courtesy of Manchester Museum